THE FORTIES

PART TWO

All Of A Sudden My Heart Sings, 3
The Anniversary Waltz, 8
Be My Love, 6
Don't Fence Me In, 14
Don't Get Around Much Any More, 11
Down In The Glen, 18
, 21
The Hill, 24
You, 28
Killarney, 32
The World On Fire, 34
Without You, 37
So Do You, 40
mental Reasons, 56
You, 52
You Very Much, 68
Ev'rything, 45
lone, 48
Song Before, 59
, 64
le, 76
sa, 73
u, 80
Affair, 84
Mama, 88
Blue Lady, 94
ed-And-Four, 90
Shoes, 97
ons, 106
Mer), 102
ourney, 109
On Love, 112
e, 116
ld Sun, 119
Magic, 122
Song Again, 128
The Trolley Song, 132
We'll Gather Lilacs, 139
We'll Keep A Welcome, 142
Yes My Darling Daughter, 145

Music processed by
Barnes Music Engraving Ltd, East Sussex TN22 4HA, UK

First published 1991
Updated edition 1996

ALL OF A SUDDEN MY HEART SINGS

Words by HAROLD ROME
Music by JAMBLAN and HENRI LAURENT HERPIN

Slow rock

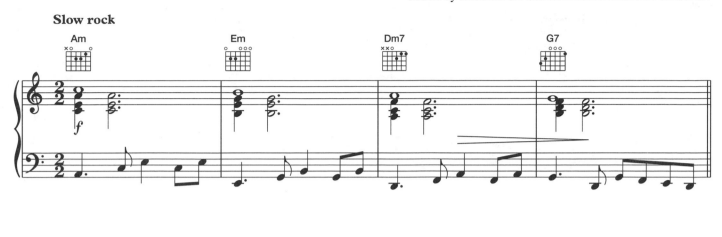

All of a sud-den my heart sings, when I re-mem-ber lit-tle things;
All of a sud-den my heart sings, when I re-mem-ber lit-tle things;

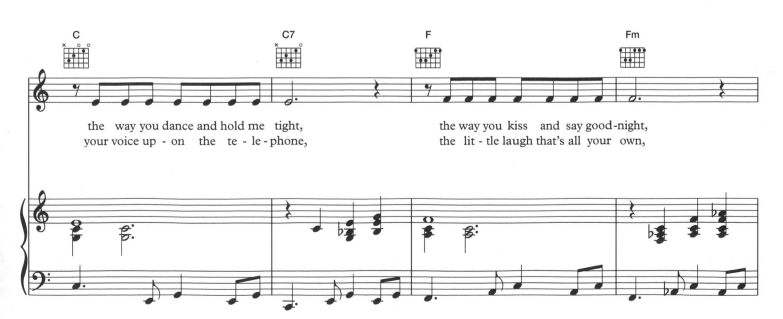

the way you dance and hold me tight, the way you kiss and say good-night,
your voice up - on the te - le-phone, the lit - tle laugh that's all your own,

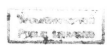

BE MY LOVE

Words by SAMMY CAHN
Music by NIKOLOUS BRODSZKY

THE ANNIVERSARY WALTZ

Words and Music by AL DUBIN and DAVE FRANKLIN

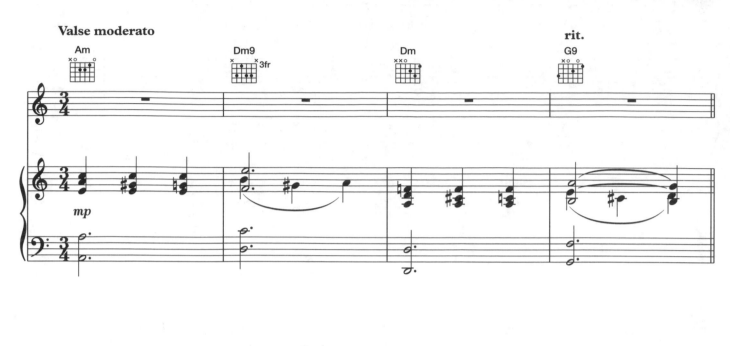

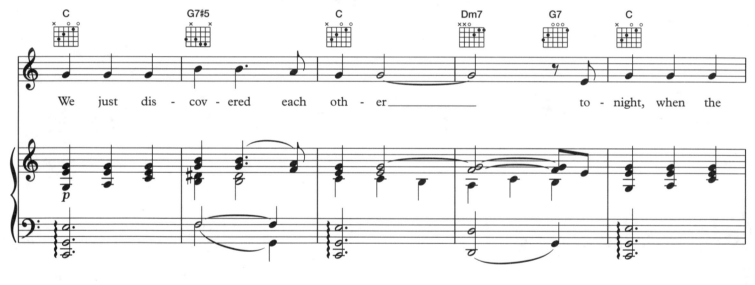

We just dis - cov - ered each oth - er_____ to - night, when the

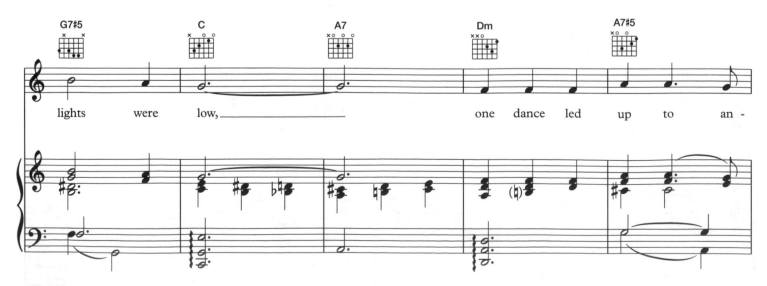

lights were low,_____ one dance led up to an -

Let this be the an - them to our fu - ture years, to

mil - lions of smiles, and a few lit - tle tears. May I

al - ways lis - ten to the An - ni - ver - sa - ry Waltz with

you. _____   you. _____

DON'T GET AROUND MUCH ANY MORE

Words by BOB RUSSELL
Music by DUKE ELLINGTON

DON'T FENCE ME IN

Words and Music by COLE PORTER

a tempo

DOWN IN THE GLEN

Words and Music by HARRY GORDON and TOMMIE CONNOR

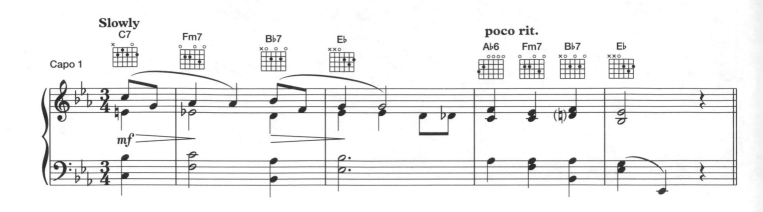

Twi - light is soft - ly fall - ing as the sun sinks in the west, the

one I love is call - ing, 'Shep - herd, come home to rest.' At

Slowly

hush of ev - en - tide, o'er the hills be - yond the Clyde, I go

roam - ing to my hea - ven down in the glen. Though

hum - ble it may be, there's an an - gel waits for me in that

lone - ly lit - tle hea - ven down in the glen. A -

DREAM

Words and Music by JOHNNY MERCER

Slowly

Get in touch with that sun-down fel-low____ as he tip-toes a-cross the sand.

He's got a mil-lion kinds of star-dust, pick your fav-ourite brand, and:

THE HEATHER ON THE HILL

Words by ALAN JAY LERNER
Music by FREDERICK LOEWE

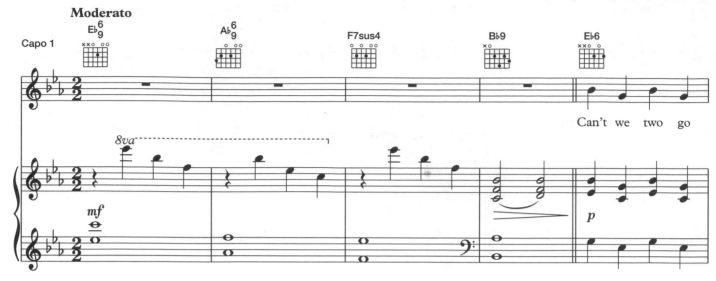

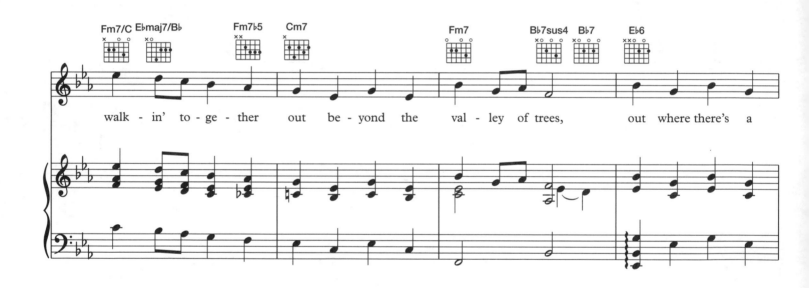

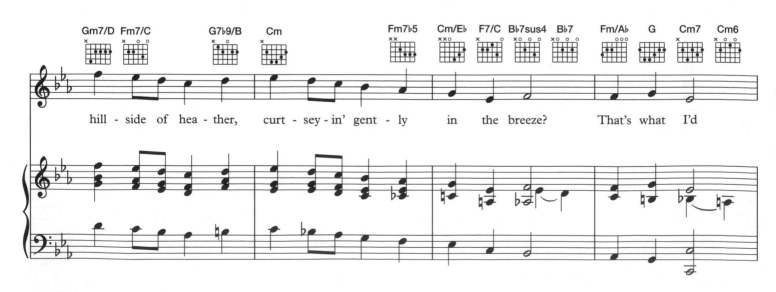

HOW ABOUT YOU

Words by RALPH FREED
Music by BURTON LANE

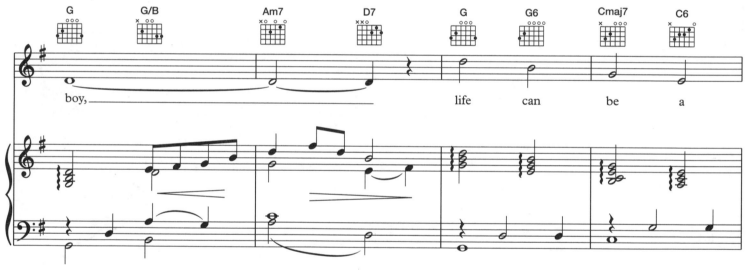

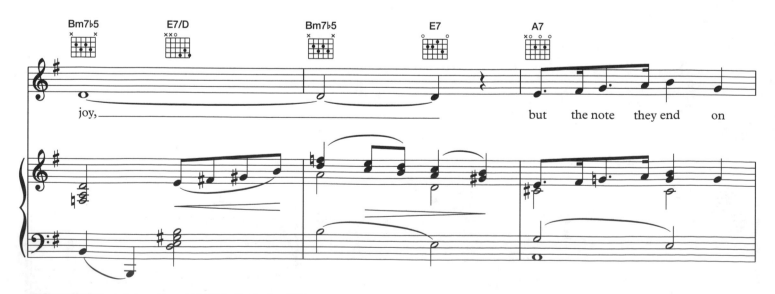

HOW CAN YOU BUY KILLARNEY

Words and Music by HAMILTON KENNEDY, FREDDIE GRANT,
GERALD MORRISON and TED STEELS

An A - me - ri - can land - ed on
'Such a won - der - ful land-scape you

E - rin's green isle, he gazed at Kil - lar - ney with rap - tur - ous smile, 'How can I buy it?' he
ne - ver have seen, a jew - el so rare t'would be - fit a - ny queen. Pride of old E - rin, a

said to his guide, 'I'll tell you how,' with a smile, he re - plied.
joy to be - hold, hea - ven on earth, far more pre - cious than gold.' 'How can you buy all the

I DON'T WANT TO SET THE WORLD ON FIRE

Words and Music by EDDIE SEILER, SOL MARCUS, BENNIE BENJAMIN
and EDDIE DURHAM

I DON'T WANT TO WALK WITHOUT YOU

Words by FRANK LOESSER
Music by JULE STYNE

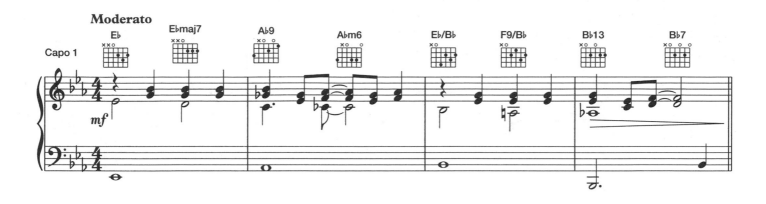

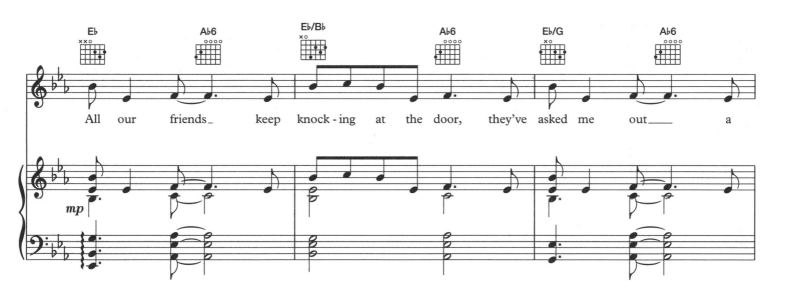

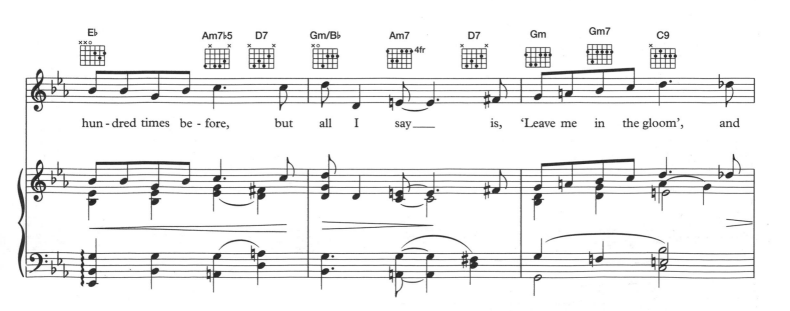

I KNOW WHY AND SO DO YOU

Words by MACK GORDON
Music by HARRY WARREN

Lyrics:
You pos-sess a ma-gic some-thing__ that has me spell-bound when you are near,

just a cer-tain charm-ing some-thing, when you're be-side me mi-ra-cles ap-pear, for

when I look at you, life's a grand il - lu - sion.

Why do rob - ins sing in De - cem - ber, long be - fore the spring - time is

due? And ev - en though it's snow - ing, vi - o - lets are grow - ing,

I'LL MAKE UP FOR EV'RYTHING

Words and Music by ROSS PARKER

Prom - is - es are ea - si - ly made, some-times they're not sin - cere, but I'm mak - ing this one from the heart, and I'll keep it too, my dear.

I'LL WALK ALONE

Words by SAMMY CAHN
Music by JULE STYNE

Moderato

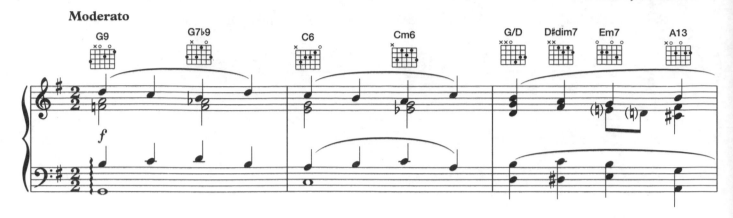

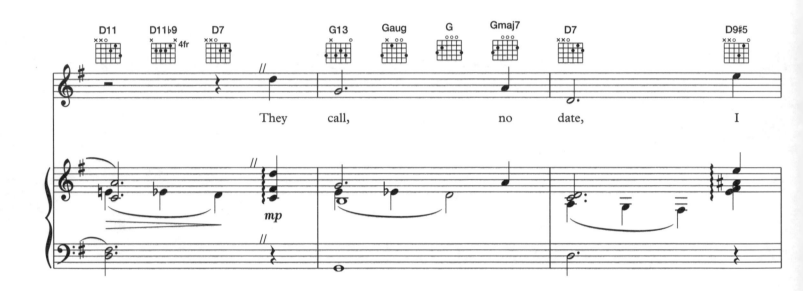

They call, no date, I

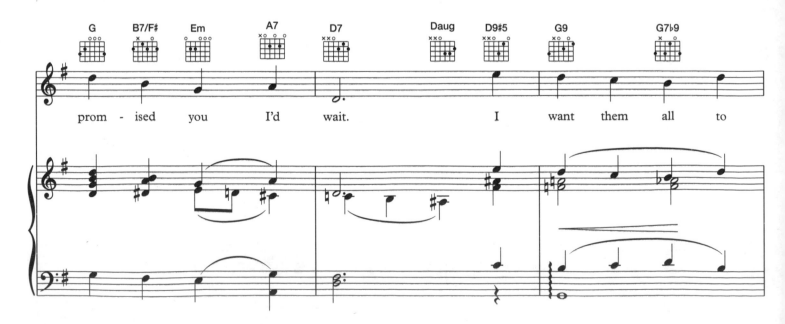

prom- ised you I'd wait. I want them all to

I REMEMBER YOU

Words by JOHNNY MERCER
Music by VICTOR SCHERTZINGER

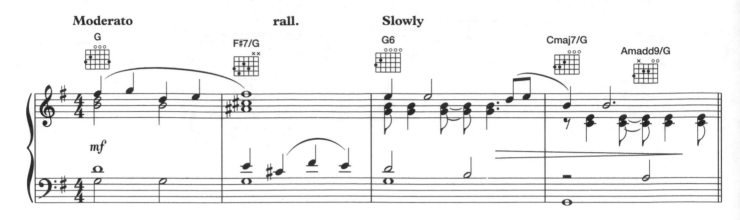

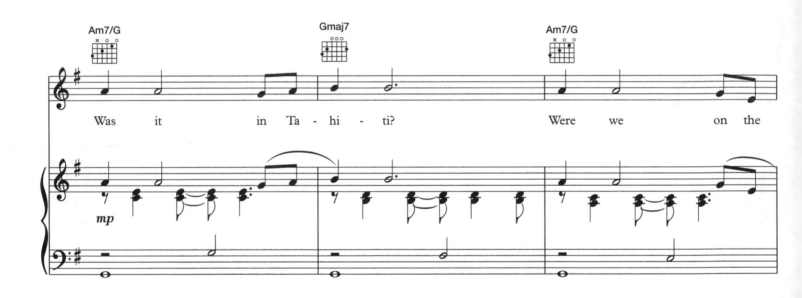

Was it in Ta - hi - ti? Were we on the

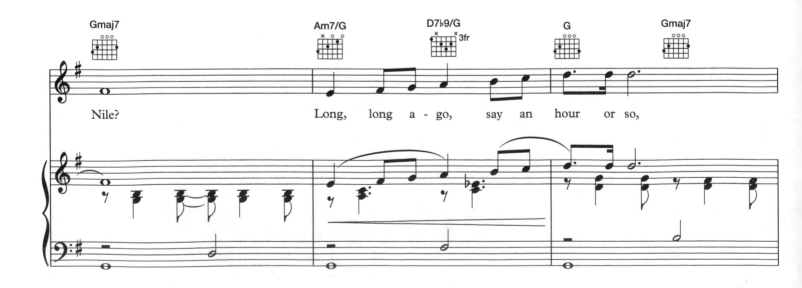

Nile? Long, long a - go, say an hour or so,

I LOVE YOU FOR SENTIMENTAL REASONS

Words by DEEK WATSON
Music by WILLIAM BEST

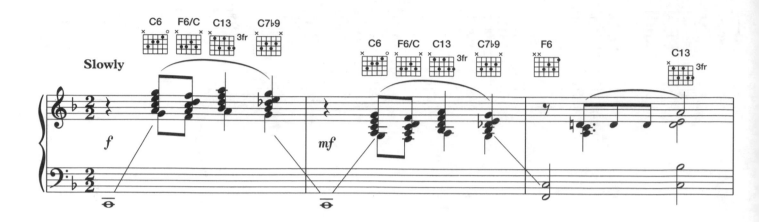

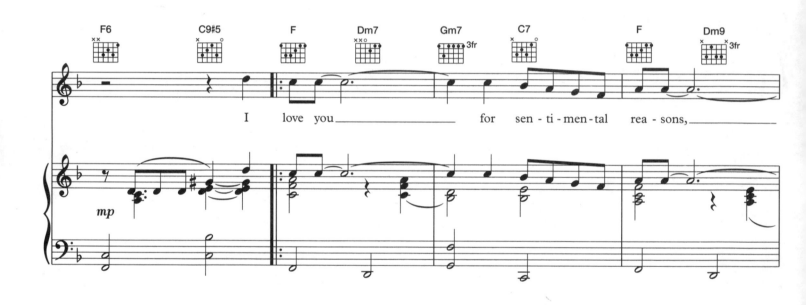

I love you _____ for sen-ti-men-tal rea-sons, _____

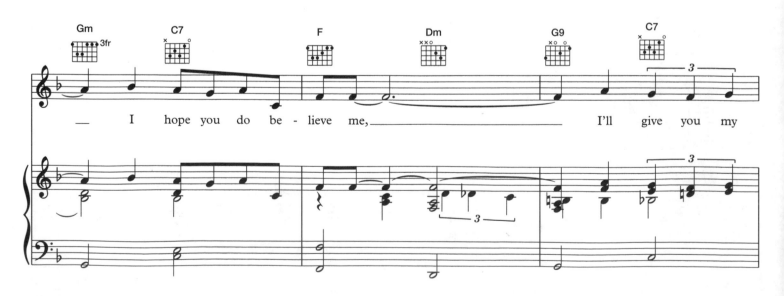

_____ I hope you do be-lieve me, _____ I'll give you my

I'VE HEARD THAT SONG BEFORE

Words and Music by JULE STYNE and SAMMY CAHN

Mu - sic helps me to re - mem - ber, _____ it helps re -

- mind me _____ of things be - hind me. _____

LAURA

Words by JOHNNY MERCER
Music by DAVID RAKSIN

I, YI, YI, YI, YI LIKE YOU VERY MUCH

Words by MACK GORDON
Music by HARRY WARREN

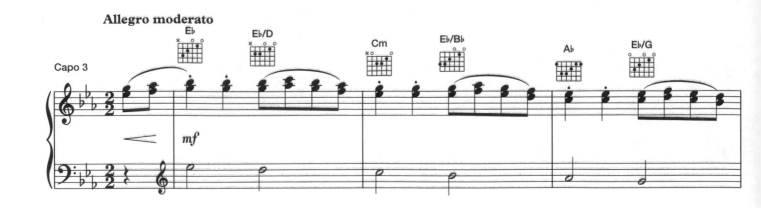

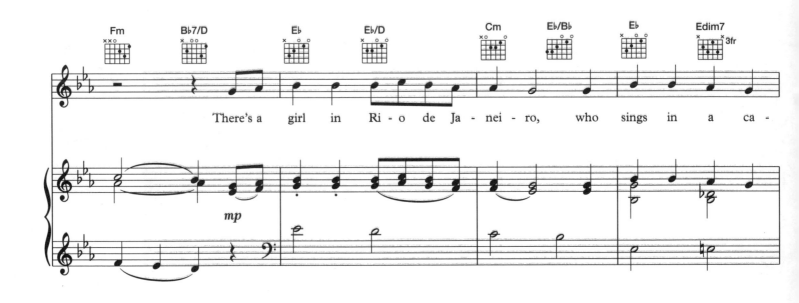

There's a girl in Ri-o de Ja-nei-ro, who sings in a ca-

-fé,_____ with a smile that's so en-tranc-ing, so sweet, so cute, so

MONA LISA

Words and Music by JAY LIVINGSTON and RAY EVANS

Slowly

Capo 1

rall.

In a vil-la in a lit-tle old I-ta-lian town,

lives a girl whose beau-ty shames the rose.

Ma-ny yearn to love her, but their

MAM'SELLE

Words by MACK GORDON
Music by EDMUND GOULDING

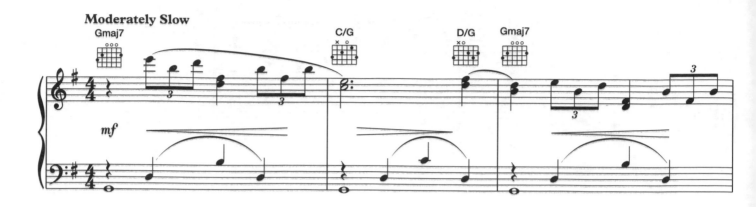

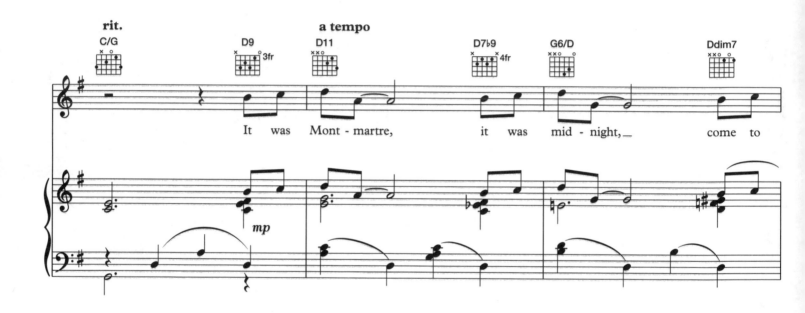

It was Mont - martre, it was mid - night,___ come to

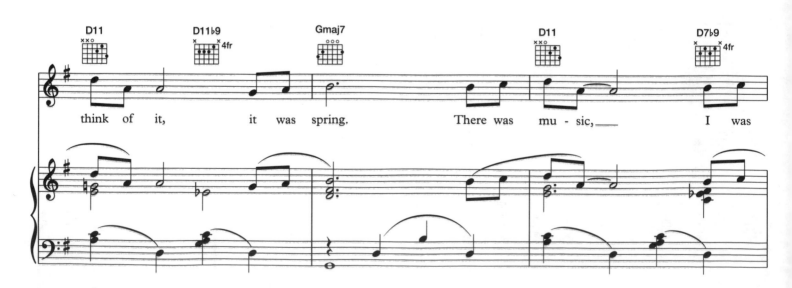

think of it, it was spring. There was mu - sic,___ I was

NEAR YOU

Words by KERMIT GOELL
Music by FRANCIS CRAIG

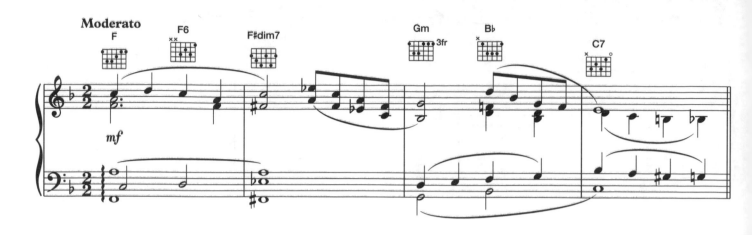

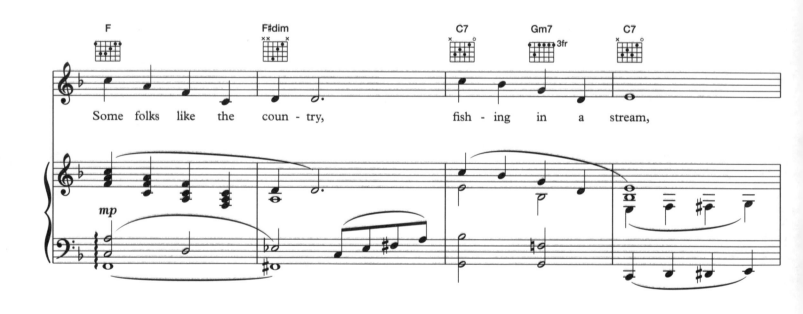

Some folks like the coun-try, fish-ing in a stream,

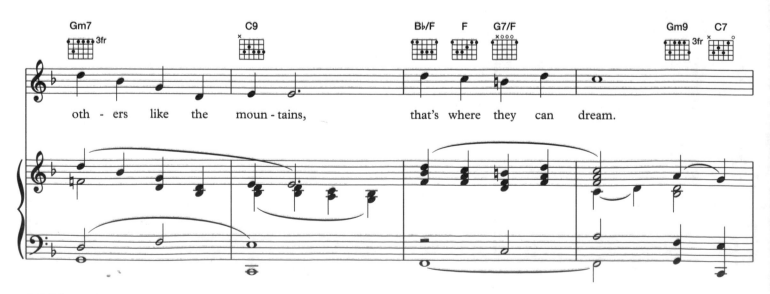

oth-ers like the moun-tains, that's where they can dream.

82

OUR LOVE AFFAIR

Words and Music by ARTHUR FREED and ROGER EDENS

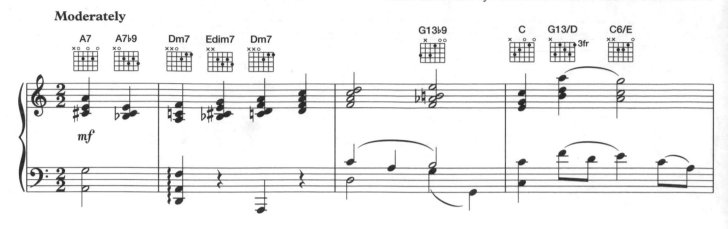

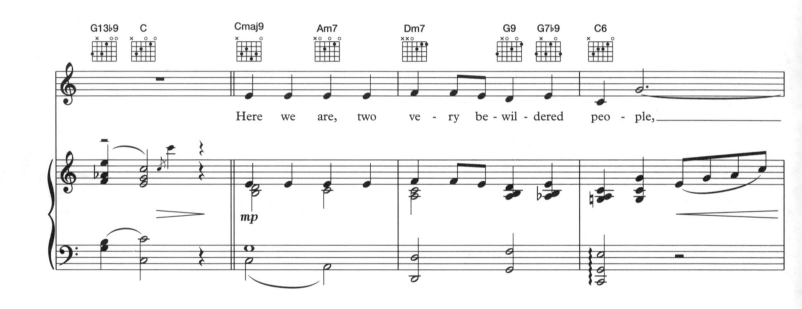

Here we are, two ve - ry be - wil - dered peo - ple,___

here we are, two babes that are lost in the wood.___

and when we're old - er, we'll proud - ly de - clare,
two hap - py peo - ple, who say on the square,

was - n't ours a love - ly love af -
is - n't ours a love - ly love af -

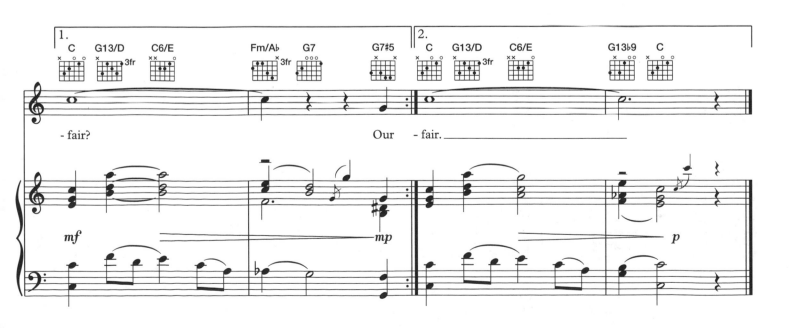

1.
- fair?

2.
Our - fair.

PISTOL PACKIN' MAMA

Words and Music by AL DEXTER

Lay that pis-tol down, babe, lay that pis-tol down, pis-tol pack-in' ma-ma,__ lay that pis-tol down!

Drink-in' beer in a ca-bar-et,__ and I was hav-in' fun! Un-

ROOM FIVE-HUNDRED-AND-FOUR

Words by ERIC MASCHWITZ
Music by GEORGE POSFORD

RED ROSES FOR A BLUE LADY

Words and Music by SID TEPPER and ROY C BENNETT

blues a - way.___ Wrap up some red ro - ses for a blue

la - dy, send them to the sweet - est gal in town,_____ and

if they do the trick, I'll hur - ry back to pick your best white or - chid

for her wed - ding gown. I want some gown.___

SAND IN MY SHOES

Words by FRANK LOESSER
Music by VICTOR SCHERTZINGER

'Out of sight, out of mind',____ that's what I told my-self.____

So I left you be - hind, and I con - trolled my-self.____

THE SEA (LA MER)

Original Words and Music by CHARLES TRENET
English Words by CARLENE MAIR

SCARLET RIBBONS

Words by JACK SEGAL
Music by EVELYN DANZIG

SENTIMENTAL JOURNEY

Slowly

Words and Music by BUD GREEN, LES BROWN and BEN HOMER

TAKING A CHANCE ON LOVE

Words by JOHN LATOUCHE and TED FETTER
Music by VERNON DUKE

TANGERINE

Words by JOHNNY MERCER
Music by VICTOR SCHERTZINGER

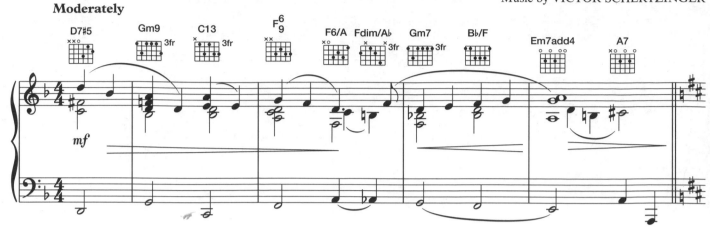

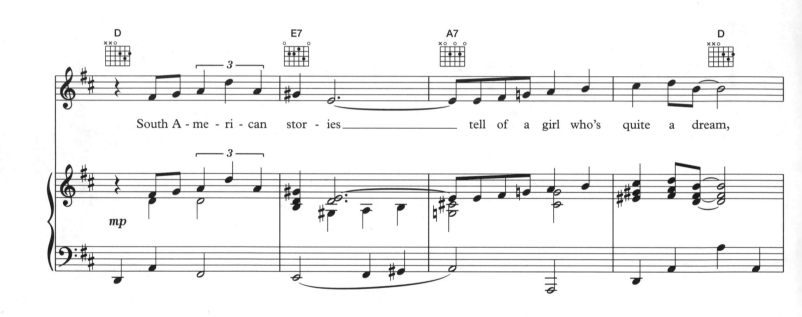

South A - me - ri - can stor - ies _____ tell of a girl who's quite a dream,

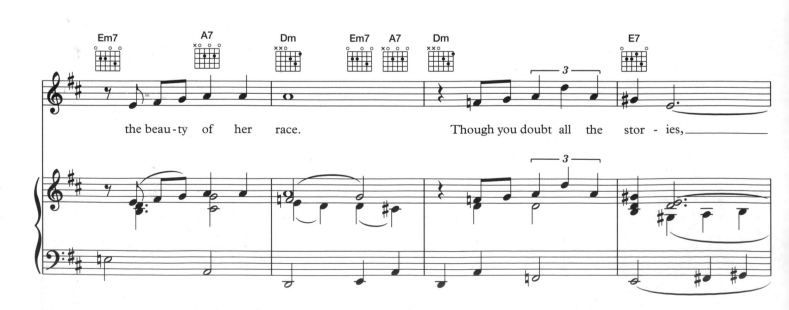

the beau - ty of her race. Though you doubt all the stor - ies, _____

118

THAT LUCKY OLD SUN

Words by HAVEN GILLESPIE
Music by BEASLEY SMITH

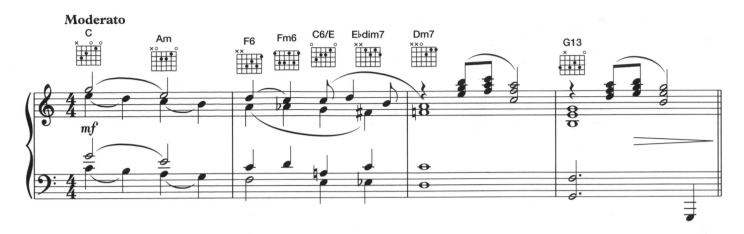

Up in the morn-in', out on the job, work like the dev-il for my

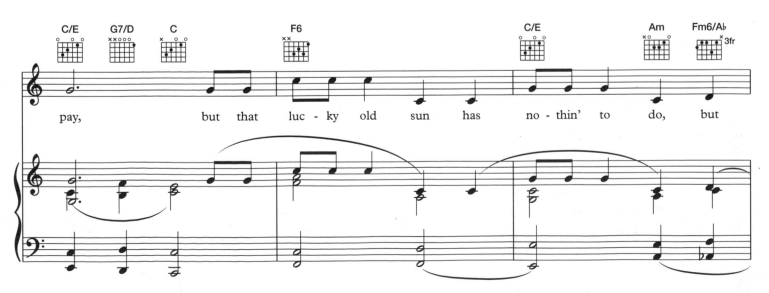

pay, but that luc-ky old sun has no-thin' to do, but

THAT OLD BLACK MAGIC

Words by JOHNNY MERCER
Music by HAROLD ARLEN

THERE GOES THAT SONG AGAIN

Words by SAMMY CAHN
Music by JULE STYNE

Moderately slow

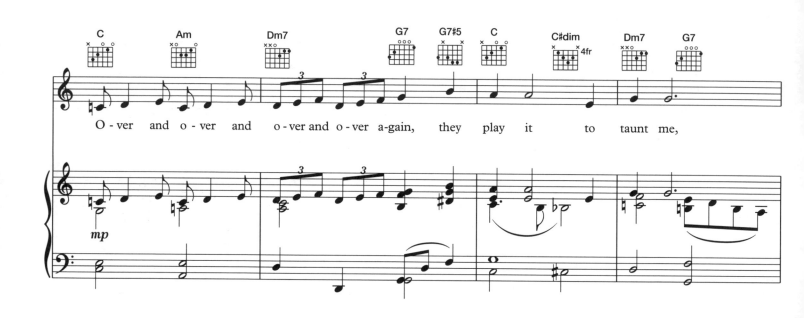

O-ver and o-ver and o-ver and o-ver a-gain, they play it to taunt me,

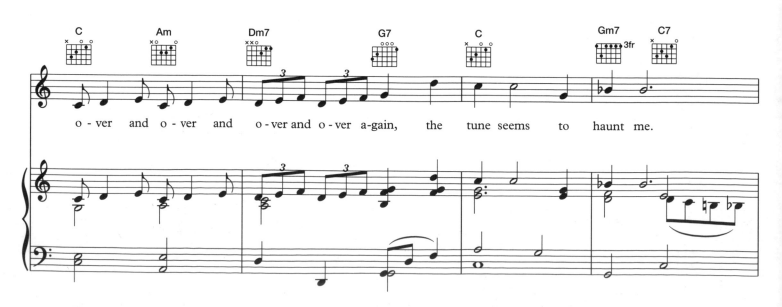

o-ver and o-ver and o-ver and o-ver a-gain, the tune seems to haunt me.

Of all the count - less me - lo - dies,_ this one stirs up me - mor - ies._

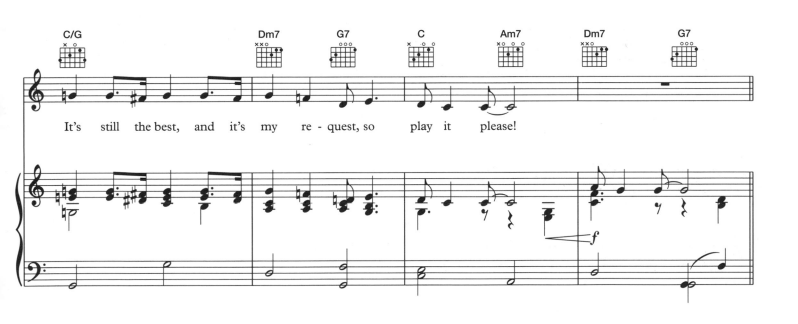

It's still the best, and it's my re - quest, so play it please!

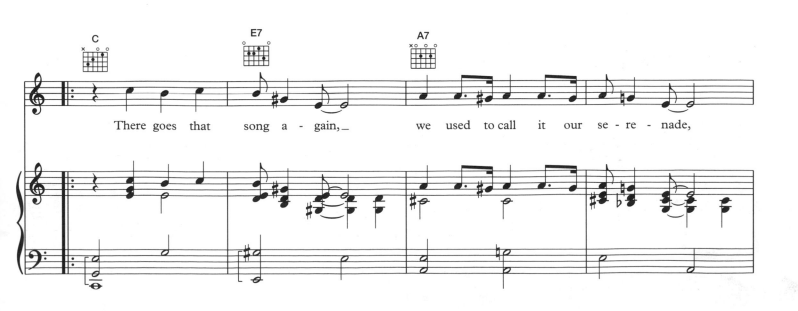

There goes that song a - gain,_ we used to call it our se - re - nade,

THE TROLLEY SONG

Words and Music by HUGH MARTIN and RALPH BLANE

134

chug', went the mo-tor,_____ 'Bump, bump, bump', went the
chug', went the mo-tor,_____ 'Bump, bump, bump', went the

Ab6/Eb   Bb7/Eb   Eb7   Ab

brake,_____ 'Thump, thump, thump', went my heart-strings,_____
brake,_____ 'Thump, thump, thump', went my heart-strings,_____

Abm   Eb6   Cm7   Fm7   Bb7   Eb6   Eb6/9

— when he smiled, I could feel the car shake._____
— when she smiled, I could feel the car shake._____

f

Fm7   Bb9   Eb6

He tipped his hat,_____ and took a seat, he said he
I tipped my hat,_____ and took a seat, I said I

mp

WE'LL GATHER LILACS

Words and Music by IVOR NOVELLO

WE'LL KEEP A WELCOME

Words by LYN JOSHUA and JAMES HARPER
Music by MAI JONES

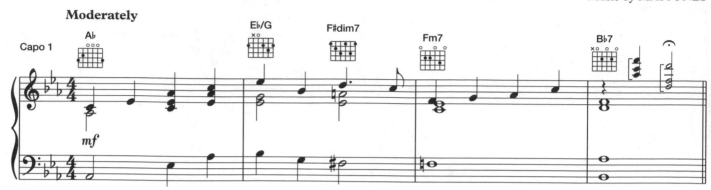

Far a - way a voice is call - ing, bells of mem - ory chime. 'Come

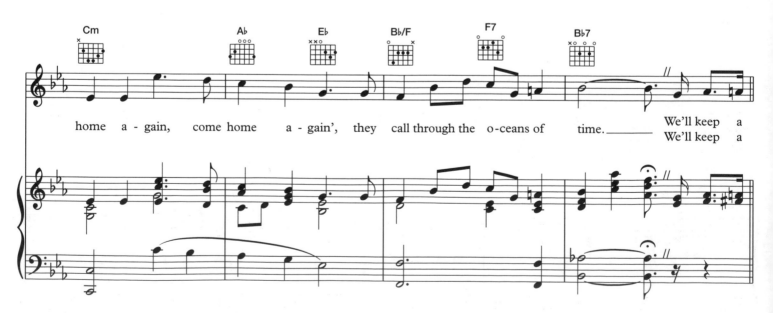

home a - gain, come home a - gain', they call through the o-ceans of time. ___ We'll keep a
We'll keep a

wel - come in the hill - side,_____ we'll keep a wel - come in the
wel - come in the hill - sides,_____ we'll keep a wel - come in the

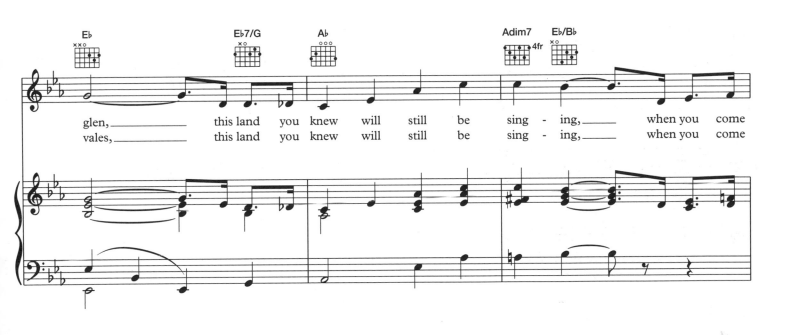

glen,_____ this land you knew will still be sing - ing,_____ when you come
vales,_____ this land you knew will still be sing - ing,_____ when you come

home sweet home a - gain._____ There'll be a friend - ly light to
home a - gain to Wales._____ This land of song will keep a

YES MY DARLING DAUGHTER

Words and Music by JACK LAWRENCE and ALBERT SIRMAY

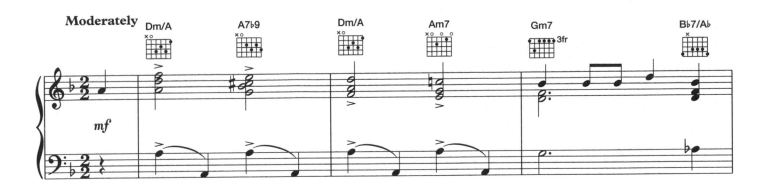

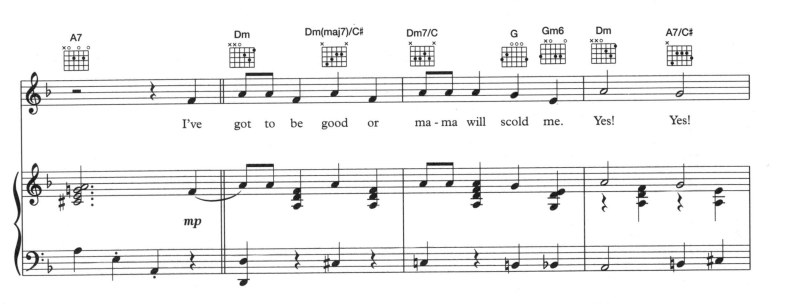

I've got to be good or ma-ma will scold me. Yes! Yes!

Yes! I asked her, and this is what she told me Yes! Yes!

146